SECRET SPACES

Judith Adams

Senior Authors
Carl B. Smith
Ronald Wardhaugh
Literature Consultant
Rudine Sims

Macmillan Publishing Co., Inc.
New York
Collier Macmillan Publishers
London

Macmillan Publishing Co., Inc.
866 Third Avenue, New York, N.Y. 10022
Collier-Macmillan Canada, Ltd.

Printed in the United States of America 11 Q

ISBN 0-02-121970-2

ACKNOWLEDGMENTS

Editor: *Kim Choi*

Designer: *Zlata Paces*

Cover Design: *Norman Gorbaty Design, Inc.* Illustrators: Ray Cruz, pp. 4-5; Guy Billout, pp. 6-21; Vladimir Fuka Hervert, pp. 24-31; Roberta Edelman, pp. 34-47; Ken Longtemps, pp. 48-49; Jackie Geyer, pp. 50-65; Susan Gilmour, pp. 74-89; Jan Pyk, pp. 98-107; Larry Ross, pp. 108-115; Tom Herbert, pp. 116-135; Vladimir Fuka Hervert, pp. 136-137.

Photo Credits: National Audubon Society, C.E. Mohr, p. 68; Photo Researchers, Russ Kinne, pp. 70, 73; United States Department of Interior, National Park Service photo by W.S. Keller, p. 71, Fred Mong, Jr., pp. 72-73; Myron Wood from Photo Researchers, pp. 92-93, 95, 96; The Bettman Archive, p. 94; Wide World Photos, pp. 96, 97.

The publisher gratefully acknowledges permission to reprint the following copyrighted material:

"The Little Green Man" reprinted from a translation of *Das Gruene Maennchen 737* by Mischa Damjan. Copyright © 1971 by Nord-Sud Verlag. Reprinted by permission of Parents' Magazine Press.

"Space" from the book *Poems of Earth and Space* by Claudia Lewis. Copyright © 1967 by Claudia Lewis. Published by E. P. Dutton & Co., Inc., and used with their permission.

"The Aquanauts" adapted from *The Aquanauts* by Arthur Schaffert. Copyright © 1971 by Arthur Schaffert. Adapted by permission of Coward, McCann and Geoghegan.

"The Fisherman Under the Sea" adapted from *The Fisherman Under the Sea* by Miyoko Matsutani. Copyright © 1969 by Parents' Magazine Press. Used by permission.

"Shells" from *I Thought I Heard the City* by Lilian Moore. Copyright © 1969 by Lilian Moore. Used by permission of Atheneum Publishers.

"Beany and Her New Recorder" adapted from *Beany and His New Recorder* by Carol Panter. Copyright © 1972 by Carol Panter. Reprinted by permission of Four Winds Press, a division of Scholastic Magazines, Inc.

"The Hammer of Thunder" adapted from *The Hammer of Thunder* by Ann Pyk. Copyright © 1972 by Ann Pyk. By permission of G. P. Putnam's Sons.

"Tee Vee" from *Catch a Little Rhyme* by Eve Merriam. Copyright © 1966 by Eve Merriam. Used by permission of Atheneum Publishers and Eve Merriam.

"The Big Pile of Dirt" adapted from *The Big Pile of Dirt* by Eleanor Clymer. Copyright © 1968 by Eleanor Clymer. Reprinted by permission of Holt, Rinehart and Winston, Inc.

Secret Spaces

CONTENTS

4

The Little Green Man

Mischa Damjan

Little Green Man Number 737 was sitting in his big soft chair and thinking. After a while, he felt hungry. Turning to the control panel, he pushed a button. Almost at once a plate came out. On it were four green pills. Number 737 ate them all and felt full right away.

"How easy life is," he thought, "—and how dull." He pushed another button on the control panel. His chair moved over to the window. Far down on the ground below were straight streets stretching as far as the eye could see. On the streets were hundreds of green people, each with two antennas. They were going every which way, but they were all standing still. Only the streets moved, carrying people here and there.

Little Green Man looked over the tops of the green houses. He could see green saucers landing and taking off to fly in the green sky.

7

Number 737 sighed and pushed another button. The chair moved over to another window. Here he could see green children in a green playground. They were playing with a cat and mouse. The cat and mouse were machines. By pushing some buttons, the children made the cat run after the mouse. But the mouse got away.

737

737

"How dull," said Number 737. "If only the mouse would run after the cat once in a while. But the machines don't work that way. If only we had some *real* animals on this planet—even a bird. Machines are so dull. I must find some fun somewhere."

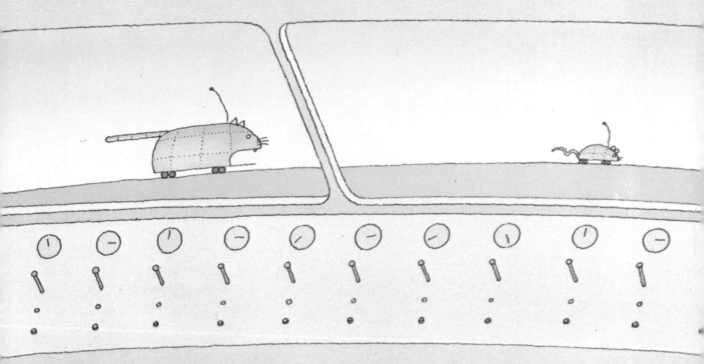

He went up to the top of his house and climbed into his flying saucer. At once it went straight up and off into space.

With great speed he flew far away from his planet, past many stars and suns. All at once, there under him lay what looked like the loveliest rug he had ever seen.

"I must land and see what that is," he said. And slowly he brought the saucer down in a very big field.

As soon as he climbed out of his ship, a strange being walked over to him. It had red hair and blue eyes, and it was wearing funny clothes.

"Hello," said the strange being. "I'm Thompson. Glad to meet you!"

"But you aren't green, and you don't have any antennas," said Number 737 with surprise. "And those animals over there," he said, pointing to a cow and two chickens. "They don't look like machines!"

Thompson laughed. "They aren't machines! The big one is my cow, Betsy, and the other two are my chickens. That's Ricky, my rooster, and Myra, my best hen." Then, taking a good look at the green man, he said, "And who are you and where did you come from?"

"I'm Number 737," he said. "I come from the Green Planet. It is many stars and suns past the Milky Way."

"Well, well," said Thompson. "You must be hungry and tired after such a long trip. Come over to the house for a bite to eat."

Number 737 was hungry. He rested in an easy chair. Thompson cooked some eggs and hot cakes and a pot of tea for his strange caller.

"What lovely pills these are!" said Number 737. "Ours are always green. What are they made of? What button did you have to push?"

Thompson laughed again. "Those aren't pills, they're eggs. And I didn't make them, Myra did. And she didn't have to push any buttons. Come, I'll show you how to eat them."

Never had 737 tasted anything so good. When he was through eating, he stretched with a sigh. He thought about the names of his new friends. Thompson . . . Betsy . . . Ricky . . . Myra . . . "I'd like a nice name, too," he said softly. "Everyone has numbers where I come from."

Thompson thought for a while. "I have it," he said. "We'll call you Zym, because that's the sound your saucer made when it came down."

"Zym . . . Zym," said the little green man. "Yes, that's a pretty name. Thank you."

It soon grew dark, and Thompson showed Zym to his room. There was a big bed with a soft down cover. Zym got in and pulled up the cover. Soon he was sound asleep. His two antennas glowed red in his sleep, because he was so happy. The animals stood around outside his window, looking in at this very strange being who had come to stay with Mr. Thompson.

A Flower for Zym

The next morning, as the sun came up, Ricky crowed to wake everyone. Then, after a big breakfast, Zym went out to watch Thompson do his work.

He was amazed to see Thompson milking the cow. But he was even more amazed to find the egg in Myra's nest.

"What kind of animals do you have on your planet?" Thompson asked him.

"Oh, we don't have room for animals any more," Zym said. "We need all the space for machines and houses and moving roads. We do have some cats and mice, but they aren't real. They are just for playing with. You push buttons, and the cat runs after the mouse. I find it very dull."

"How sad not to have any animals," said Thompson. "But come, let's look around a bit."

As they got to the field, Zym stopped short. "What is that? It looks like a small sun on the end of a green stick," he cried.

"It's a sunflower," said Thompson. "It's called that because it looks like the sun. It likes to turn its face to look at the sun."

"How beautiful!" said Zym with joy. "Do you mind if I just watch this wonderful flower all day?"

While Thompson went off to plow in his fields, Zym watched the sunflower.

When Thompson came back later in the afternoon, he looked very tired.

"Poor man," said Zym. "Why do you have to work so hard?"

"It's the rocks in my field," said his friend. "Every year it gets harder and harder to plow around them."

"Ho! You have been so kind to me. Now I can pay you back," said Zym. He went to his saucer and came back carrying a strange machine.

"This is a ray gun," he said to Thompson. "I'll make short work of those rocks."

He turned it on, and each time the ray hit a rock it turned the rock into fine sand.

"How can I ever thank you!" cried Thompson. "What can I give you to pay you back for your help?"

"There is only one thing I want to take home with me," said Zym. "And that's the beautiful sunflower."

Zym and Thompson were hungry after their long day. They ate a good supper that evening. Later, as they rested, Thompson asked Zym about his planet.

"Why don't you come with me and see for yourself?" said Zym. "I would like Myra to come, too, so that my friends can see how she makes her pills."

17

Off they all went together, and Zym made sure he brought along his sunflower.

In no time at all they were coming in for a landing. Zym had wired ahead to his planet that he was bringing a very special friend. By the time they landed, there were hundreds of green people waiting. Thompson had never seen so much green in all his life. And the people of the Green Planet had never seen anything like Thompson. They stared at his red hair, blue eyes, and strange clothes.

Zym told them about what happened to him on Earth. He also told them how kind his friend had been to him. "Now I must show you a most wonderful thing," he said.

While everyone came around, a box was brought, filled with green straw. Myra sat on the straw. In a short time she hopped up and made a sound as if she were saying, "Look-look-look what I did! Look-look-look what I did!"

Zym held up a beautiful white egg for all to see. Thompson and Zym left the amazed people of the Green Planet to look at the egg. They went to Zym's house. In a big pot filled with green earth, they planted the sunflower. It looked lovely in the middle of all that green.

That night Thompson cooked the egg for Zym while Zym gave Thompson a supper of green pills. Thompson found the taste of the pills very strange, but they did fill him up.

20

While Thompson was away, the animals back home were beginning to worry. They had seen Thompson fly out of sight in the flying saucer, and they were afraid they might never see him again. All night long they watched the sky. But there was no need to worry. The next morning there was the saucer back in the field, with Zym and Thompson climbing out.

"I must return at once," said Zym. "But I will come to see you again. I really will."

Thompson threw his arms around his new friend. "Yes, yes," he said. "I will have more sunflowers for you. Also I will give you a chicken for your very own."

Then, with a loud *zym* sound, the saucer went off into space.

I like the word, space,
A mighty word
With room for ace and pace and even Cape
Between its s and e;
A word suggesting air and race,
Expanse, escape,
Mystery.
In short,
Suggesting
SPACE,
That magnificent
Place.

—Claudia Lewis

23

The Aquanauts

Arthur Schaffert

The astronaut flies far away from earth to explore space, the moon, and —maybe someday—other worlds. The aquanaut goes to the floor of the sea to explore places just as wonderful and strange as the astronaut's.

You may have seen some of the beautiful fish that swim in the ocean. If you were an aquanaut, you could go far under water and stay there long enough to see many unusual creatures. You would find things you never even dreamed of.

The only way you can stay under water for more than a short time is by using special gear—the kind of gear used by aquanauts.

Pretend you are an aquanaut. What gear will you need? You will need an air tank, flippers, a face mask, a heavy belt, and a waterproof watch.

The air tank gives you air to breathe under water. You wear the tank on your back. A short hose from the tank brings the air to your mouth. Before you dive, a lot of air is pumped into your tank. As more and more air is pumped in, the tank gets full of air under pressure. The tank can hold enough air for you to breathe under water for about an hour.

You wear the flippers on your feet. They help you swim quickly under water without having to use your hands.

The face mask helps you see without getting water in your eyes.

The heavy belt keeps your body under water.

A waterproof watch helps you make sure you don't stay down longer than an hour.

It's also important to have a friend with you when you dive. That way you can help each other under water.

Now you are ready. You have your tank full of air, flippers on your feet, the mask on your face, a waterproof watch, and a friend to dive with you.

JUMP IN!

As you go down, water pushes in on your body from all sides. As you go deeper, the pressure from the water around you becomes greater. Now you have to breathe in more air. One end of the hose is in your mouth. At the end there is a valve. The valve opens and closes like a little door. More pressure from the water around you makes the valve open up more, so you breathe in more air. In this way, the pressure inside your body grows. Now you can stand the pressure of the water because the pressure inside your body is the same as it is outside.

As soon as you get under water, you will be able to see the bright and beautiful colors of the fish. Deeper down, everything looks blue or green. Sunlight does not go down very deep into the water, so it is harder to see colors. It is also much colder down deep.

Many of the fish you will see swim together in schools, looking for food. Most of them are friendly. You might see many unusual fish. You might see a big, flat fish that looks as if it had wings. Or you might see a sea horse, that swims around with its head up and its tail down. It carries baby sea horses in a pocket on its front. There are many different creatures in the sea.

Maybe an octopus will come out from where it hides in the rocks on the bottom. Waving all eight arms, it will swim away from you very fast. If you go after the octopus, it will shoot out a spray of ink. While you're watching this dark cloud, the octopus will swim away.

Somewhere along the floor of the ocean, where it's not so deep or cold, you might find some beautiful coral shapes. Shapes like fans, branches, and flowers arc made by tiny animals inside the coral.

29

Now your hour is almost over, and
it is time to go up. As you swim slowly
to the top, the pressure gets lighter
and the water feels warmer. The top of
the water looks like a wavy mirror. At
last your head comes out. Now you can
take off your face mask and breathe the
air around you.

Soon aquanauts will not have to dive
to the ocean floor and come up again
every day. They will be able to live
in underwater houses. Air will be pumped into their houses through a long hose.

Some aquanauts have already lived
and worked under water for many days.
Wearing their gear, the aquanauts went
out of the underwater house to learn
more about underwater life. They took
pictures of coral. They gathered rocks
on the ocean floor. They looked for
signs of oil and minerals. They followed

fish to watch them feed and lay their eggs. They learned a lot about life on the ocean floor.

A good part of our earth is covered by seas and oceans. People explore the underwater world for more than just fun. There are many things we find in the sea that we can use. We can grow food in the sea. We can use seaweed for drugs. There is even a jelly made from seaweed that is used in making ice cream!

Scientists are also learning that many minerals can be taken from the sea bottom. They have found oil under the ocean floor.

In the world that the aquanaut explores, there are many wonderful things that everyone may someday share. Maybe, in time, you will explore this world for yourself.

Americans of the Past

Here is someone about your age thinking of life in the time of the Aztecs, a people who lived in central Mexico hundreds of years ago.

First the boy dreams of being a cacique (kə-sḗ-kə), a chieftain. Perhaps the cacique will lead a group up the pyramid. If you were a cacique, would you wear a headdress? How could you make a headdress?

Next he imagines a pyramid. Pretend you are climbing a pyramid. Move your legs!

Finally, the boy imagines he is an artist who decorates walls with designs and drawings. What do you see in the Aztec drawings? Can you draw pictures and designs that look like that?

The Fisherman Under the Sea

MIYOKO MATSUTANI

Long ago there lived a good-looking young man named Taro Urashima. He was a fisherman. And he lived in a village near the sea. Each day he set out in his boat to catch fish to sell.

One day he went out to sea as always. In the whole day he did not catch even one fish. Returning that night, he came upon some noisy children. They were standing over a little turtle. They were having great fun, banging on the poor creature's shell and swinging it by the tail.

Taro was touched with pity when he saw this. He asked the children to let the turtle go. They were sorry about their treatment of the turtle. They gave the animal to Taro and ran off down the beach.

The fisherman now took a better look at the turtle. He was surprised to find that it was like no other turtle he had ever seen. Its shell glowed with color. At last he put the turtle down by the edge of the water. The creature quickly crawled into the waves, where it would be safe. Taro watched.

Then, just as he turned to leave, the turtle appeared again. It shook its head up and down as if to say *thank you*.

The next day Taro set out again to fish. "Let us hope that today is a lucky day for me," he said to himself. He put his net into the water.

But just then a very big turtle appeared at the edge of the boat. Bowing his head, he spoke to the amazed fisherman.

"I have come to thank you for saving the life of a small turtle," he said. "I have been told by my master, the King of the Sea, to take you down to his Dragon Palace. He wants to thank you, also. Would you be so kind as to climb on my back?"

Taro was so surprised that he did not think to say no. He jumped from his boat and quickly sat down on the turtle's back. Slowly the creature turned around. They swam down, down into the blue-green water of the sea.

All around Taro were fish of every kind and color. Strange seaweed floated in the water around him. Soon Taro and the turtle were in an underwater land of great mountains and valleys. Then, ahead of them, appeared the glowing walls of a palace. It was the Dragon Palace of the King of the Sea. The building, with its coral walls and a roof of lovely sea shells, glowed in the water.

Taro Urashima pulled in his breath with surprise. Never had the fisherman seen anything so beautiful. Servants appeared at the doorway, and he was shown into the palace. The servants showed Taro from one room to another. Each room was more beautiful than the last. Finally Taro was shown into the throne room.

There before him sat the King of the Sea. At once Taro got on his knees and bent his head before such a wonderful sight.

"Please do not bow before me," said the king kindly. "I have had you brought here so that I might thank you for saving the life of my daughter."

With this, a young girl came in and
bowed before Taro. "I was the small
turtle you saved from the children,"
she said. Her voice was like the soft
sound of far-off bells.

Taro was without words before such a beautiful girl. The princess moved like sea grass waving in the water. Her smile was as soft as the sea waves on a quiet day.

Seeing the puzzled look in Taro's eyes, she said, "I had never gone out of my home here in the Dragon Palace. I wanted to see the people who live on the land. I turned myself into a little turtle and swam to the shore of your village. But as soon as I had crawled up to the edge of the beach, I was found by those children. If you had not saved me from them, I would have come to a sad end."

Before Taro could say anything, she went on. "But I forget. You must be hungry after your long trip."

She waved her hand, and all at once there appeared a table covered with all kinds of wonderful food. In all his life, Taro had never tasted such food. The fish had a strange and wonderful taste. The cakes were as light as snow. The plates were of the best gold and silver. Also the food was brought in pots of glowing red.

Taro had hardly started to eat when the princess waved her hand again. At once, the sound of beautiful music filled the hall.

When the party was over, the princess took him by the hand. She showed him through the many rooms of the palace. After a while they came to a big window looking out upon wide fields.

It was spring. Taro could see the farmers busy planting their young rice. But as he looked the plants grew almost at once. The countryside turned from the light green of the spring to the dark green of summer. He was no sooner amazed by this when he saw that the rice plants were bent over, heavy with grain. Fall had come. Hardly was the grain picked when the snows of winter began to fall. In no more than a second, a whole year had appeared before his eyes!

The Lacquer Box

And so the time went by for Taro in the Dragon Palace under the sea. Never had he been so happy. The beautiful princess became his beloved wife. There were servants to fill his every wish. He could not tell if it was real or just a dream.

But one day, Taro suddenly remembered his fishing boat. He remembered the joy of pulling nets filled with fish up out of the sea. He thought of his mother and his friends in the village. How he would like to see them all! How he would love to tell of his life here in the palace! He went to the princess and told her of his wish to see his village once more.

It made the princess sad to hear Taro's wish. But she saw that he had made up his mind. Sadly she decided to let him go. "But take this with you," she said, handing him a box of the best red lacquer. "As long as you keep this safe, you will always be able to come back to me." Then she stopped. "But you must promise never to open the box to see what is in it," she said.

Taro held his wife close. He promised that he would never open the box. He also promised he would return soon. Then, with the good wishes of the King of the Sea, he set out from the Dragon Palace.

Once more Taro climbed on the back of the big turtle. They began the trip to his own land. Suddenly he could no longer see the walls of the palace.

Through the valleys and past the mountains they went, then up, up to the top of the sea. There before him Taro saw again the houses of his village beside the sea.

He thanked the turtle for his safe trip. Then he ran up the beach to his village. But something was wrong! The mountains behind the village were still there, but the streets and houses all looked different. Taro walked through the strange streets to where his house should have been. But there was a house he had never seen before.

Going up to a villager, he asked, "Is this not the place where Taro Urashima lives?"

The man looked at him with surprise.

"Taro Urashima's house fell down many years ago," he said. "When I was a boy, my grandfather told me a story that his grandfather had told him," the villager said. "Taro Urashima went off fishing one morning and was never seen again. His boat was found, but not Taro. People thought that awful sea creatures had taken him away."

With a word of thanks, Taro turned from the villager. He walked back to the seashore. How many years had he lived in the Dragon Palace? A hundred? Two hundred? But here he was, still a young man! He was suddenly very lonely. His eyes fell on the red lacquer box. Forgetting what the princess had told him, Taro took off the string that went around the box. He opened it.

White dust appeared as he opened
the box. All at once Taro became an
old man with white hair and a long
white beard.

Then, softly, from over the water, he
heard the sad voice of the princess.
"Oh, Taro, Taro, my husband, my
beloved. You promised me that you
would never open the lacquer box. It
was your life I had closed up in the
box so that you would never grow old.
Farewell, Taro. Farewell, beloved, farewell."

And then the voice of the princess
was lost. Taro, an old man, could hear
only the sound of the sea waves as
they hit the beach at his feet.

SHELLS

The bones of the sea
are on the shore,
shells
curled into the sand,
shells
caught in green weed hair.
All day I gather them
and there are always
more.

I take them home,
magic bones of the sea,
and when
I touch one,
then I hear
I taste
I smell the sea
again.

— Lilian Moore

49

Beany and Her New Recorder

Carol Panter

Beany Parker was a special kind of girl. Pomponio was a special kind of cat. Beany and Pomponio hung out together whenever they could. They took walks together and climbed trees in the woods. They even managed to sleep together.

There were certain things in Beany's life which cats could not share. And there were certain things in Pomponio's life which girls could not share. But Beany and Pomponio tried to share as many things as they could. Happily, they managed to be together most of the time.

Everyone in Beany's family was a fine musician. In the afternoon, Beany's mother cooked dinner. The rest of the family went off to different corners of the house to practice their music.

Beany did her practicing in the laundry room. Pomponio went with her. Beany's instrument was a beautiful wooden recorder. The recorder had a mouthpiece for blowing and seven airholes. Also there was one airhole underneath which was meant just for her thumb. Beany was a good player. She knew what to do to make the right notes come out at the right time.

Pomponio hid in the laundry basket when Beany played.

One day Beany's father said, "You're becoming a good musician, Beany. I think I should look around for another recorder for you. It will be an instrument that is even better than the one you have now."

"Wow," Beany thought to herself. She practiced her music all over again.

Pomponio hid in the laundry basket again.

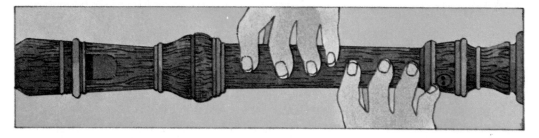

Beany's brother Sam had the best place to practice. Sam was the family keyboard player. That meant he always got the first turn at the **harpsichord**. The harpsichord looked like a small piano. But its sound was very different. When Sam struck a key with his finger, a piece of wood inside the harpsichord shot out. Then it plucked the string that he wanted. This sound was short and soft.

Sam was always playing one thing or another. Sometimes he played from printed music. Sometimes he played things which he made up himself. The harpsichord really belonged to the whole family. But Sam pretended that it belonged to him.

In the evenings and on weekends, Beany's father practiced downstairs in the mud room. The name of his instrument was the **viola da gamba.** The viola da gamba is an instrument like a cello, but with six strings. Mr. Parker always worried over them. He tuned and plucked them again and again.

"The mud room is such a cold place to practice," Beany's mother often said to her father. "You'd better wear warm clothes down there."

Beany's father wore a coat when he practiced. Often he wore a bright scarf around his neck. Mr. Parker moved the bow across the strings of the viola da gamba. He drew out the deep, sweet-singing music. The end of his bright scarf swung back and forth, keeping the beat very well.

Beany's mother called from the kitchen. "F *sharp*, Beany. That should have been an F *sharp*. And please tell your father that dinner is ready."

Beany's mother was a singer. She had a lovely, light voice. Mrs. Parker, luckily, could practice all through the day. She sang one song while she was watering the plants. She sang another song while she was driving the car. And still another one while she was working in the yard.

Besides being a singer, Beany's mother could play the recorder and the piano. She was some mother! Beany also loved her cooking.

And so did Pomponio.

After dinner, the Parkers gathered around the harpsichord with their chairs and their music stands. It was the time of day that no one wanted to miss. The Parker family played together. The beautiful sound filled the room.

Pomponio stretched out nearby. The music of Handel made him yawn.

The Legend

One day Beany's father said, "I have a surprise for you."

Her mother and brother gathered around. And so did Pomponio. They must have known something was up. Beany's father handed her a long, thin box. "You've become a very fine recorder player, Beany," her father said. "I thought it was time to find you a very fine instrument, as I said I would."

Beany couldn't say a word. "Open it," said Mr. Parker.

Beany opened the box. She could see right away that this was a most unusual recorder.

"The recorder was made in Venice, Beany," her father told her. "And it's very, very old."

"So don't lose it," said Sam, helpfully.

"There's another thing, Beany," said Mr. Parker. "A legend from long ago comes with your recorder. The man who sold it to me asked that I pass the legend on to you."

"What is it?"

"It goes like this," Beany's father said.

> "Play ye this pipe
>
> With joy in your heart
>
> And a bird in a tree
>
> Shall join in."

"It means that if you feel happy and you take your recorder to the woods, a bird will sing along with you," said Sam.

"Wow," Beany said, "Do you think the legend is true? Do you think a bird will really sing along?"

"I would certainly expect the legend to be true," said Mr. Parker.

Beany took her beautiful new recorder and went to the woods behind her house. She picked one of her special places to sit. It was a large, flat rock near the trees.

"Come on, Pomponio," Beany called. "We'll be comfortable here."

Then Beany placed her new recorder to her mouth. She placed her fingers on the airholes. And she placed her thumb on the airhole hidden underneath. She began to play. Oh, what a wonderful sound came from this old instrument! And to think it was her very own. It belonged to *her*. Beany felt great joy in her heart. She played and played.

The woods were very quiet. Beany stopped and listened carefully. Beany did not hear one bird.

The next day Beany tried again. But this time she picked a different place to sit. It was a less comfortable place. But it was one that was near the biggest tree in the woods. The tree held the nests of many families of birds.

Beany played and played. It was the music of Bach. The sound was so lovely that it brought joy to Beany's heart. But not one bird sang.

Beany had another idea. She climbed to the other end of the woods. She took out her recorder. Maybe birds don't like Bach, she thought. Maybe that's why none of them sang. Beany played the music of Corelli. Again it brought joy to her heart. A rabbit stopped to listen for a while and then ran off.

But no bird sang for Beany.

After that, Beany stopped trying. But she couldn't stop thinking about her problem. Why didn't the birds sing?

The next day, the Parker family gathered with their instruments for music time. Pomponio sat on the harpsichord, carefully cleaning his paws.

"Beany doesn't seem happy tonight," said her mother.

"She's got birds on the brain," said Sam. He wanted to start playing.

Mr. Parker shook his long bow at Sam. Then he asked, "They've never sung yet, Beany?"

"Never," said Beany softly. She felt very sad.

"I wonder if we couldn't find out what's gone wrong. You should, by the legend, have joy in your heart, Beany," her father said. "Are you sure you've had it while you were playing?"

"Yes, I'm sure," Beany said, even though it was gone right now.

"Where are the birds while you're playing, Beany? What are they doing if they're not singing?" asked her mother.

"I don't know," Beany said. "I never see them. They seem to be hiding."

"Maybe they don't like you," Sam said. Again, Mr. Parker shook his bow at Sam.

But what Sam said gave Beany an idea. "What could it be that might stop a bird from singing, I wonder? It's only me, and the recorder, and Pomp-"

All of a sudden Beany took her recorder and started out of the house. Pomponio ran after her.

"Come on, Pomponio," Beany said, holding the door open. "Let's find out what's true and what isn't."

They raced off to the woods. Beany made herself comfortable on the large rock near the trees.

"Pomponio," Beany said, "will you hide in that pile of leaves over there? I'd like to try something."

Pomponio stretched each leg slowly. He seemed to be thinking.

"Pomponio," Beany said, "I think I'll play some Handel. And after that, some Scarlatti."

Beany played. Pomponio yawned when he heard the Handel. But at the first note of Scarlatti he hid deep down in the pile of leaves. Not even the tip of his tail was in sight.

"Pomponio," Beany said lovingly, "you are a most unmusical cat."

Then Beany took her new recorder and began to play again. The beautiful sound floated high up into the leafy green branches. Beany played and played. She felt great joy in her heart.

Suddenly, from a tree far in the woods, came the singing of a bird. It was a clear singing which went along with Beany and her beautiful new recorder. They filled the woods with the most lovely music.

"Mother, Daddy, Sam," Beany called into the house, "It's true! The legend is true! A bird in the woods did join in!"

"We heard it, Beany," they answered. "What wonderful music you made together!"

Pomponio climbed out of the leaves, rolled over, yawned and fell asleep.

Same Space, Same Place

Some people find a place for themselves and never leave it! This poem is about two people who sit in front of the TV all the time. Of course, the poem is just for fun. People don't really sit **all** the time in front of a TV—or do they?

Tee Vee

girls   In the house
of Mr. and Mrs. Spouse

boys   he and she
would watch teevee

girls   and never a word
between them spoken

boys   until the day
the set was broken.

A boy   Then "How do you do?"
said he to she,
"I don't believe
that we've met yet.
Spouse is my name.
What's yours?" he asked.

A girl   "Why, mine's the same!"
Said she to he,
"Do you suppose that we could be...?"

All   But the set came suddenly right about,
and so they never did find out.

—Eve Merriam

67

Nature's Dark World

Judith Adams

You open your eyes wide, stretch out your arms, and try hard to see your fingers. But you can't see anything! It is pitch dark—much darker than when you go outdoors at night and close your eyes.

And it is very, very still. All you can hear is the soft sound of water as it drips from somewhere.

There are lizards, snails, bugs, fish, bats, and other animals moving around, not very far from where you stand. But these creatures don't make much noise. You don't hear them.

Where is this place? It is the underground world of a cave.

What is a cave? A cave is a natural hole in the earth. It can be a very small space, or it can be miles long and many feet high. But a true cave *must* be made by nature.

Nature makes caves in different ways. Wind caves are formed in the sides of mountains by the wind blowing small bits of sand against the rock. After a long, long time, deep holes appear in the rock.

Sea caves are formed by waves which have beat against the rock for hundreds and hundreds of years. Some of these caves are deep under water. People have explored these underwater caves. They have found wonderful plant and animal life there.

Ice caves are caves that are so cold that ice has formed over everything, making lovely shapes everywhere.

But you are not in a wind cave, a sea cave, or an ice cave: you are in a cave made in a soft rock called *limestone*.

Most caves are made of limestone. Limestone lies under a good part of the earth. Limestone caves are formed when water drips slowly through cracks in the rock. Over many years the water melts the rock and makes holes in it. The holes become bigger and bigger, until a cave is formed.

A small hole in limestone takes hundreds of years to form. And there are some big rock caves that took millions of years to form! Millions of years! As long as water keeps dripping into a limestone cave, the cave is still being formed.

Listen closely to the dripping water. Turn your light on it. See——it is running down from the cave roof and along the walls of the cave. And look! What beautiful shapes there are, hanging from the roof of the cave! They look like icicles. But they aren't icicles at all. These shapes are called *stalactites*. They have been formed by water and limestone that have dripped down from the roof of the cave.

Do you see the shapes coming up from the floor of the cave? They look very much like stalactites, don't they? These shapes are called *stalagmites.* They have been formed by limestone and water that have dripped onto the floor of the cave. Some of these stalagmites look a little like birthday cakes!

Sometimes a stalactite and a stalagmite grow together to form one long shape. Sometimes a row of stalactites may join sideways to form what looks like a curtain. Think of how many millions of years it would have taken a curtain of stalactites to form. It can take a stalactite a whole year to grow as wide as a hair!

Every cave is different inside. Some have streams and rivers running through them. In some caves, there is enough water dripping down the walls to make a lovely waterfall. You can walk right into some caves; others drop down many feet as soon as you go through the opening.

You'd better not try to explore caves that drop suddenly!

The temperature in a cave is always the same. If the temperature above ground is always hot, the cave temperature will be always hot. If the temperature above ground is always cold, the temperature in the cave will always be cold. And if the temperature above ground is different in summer and winter, the temperature in the cave will be somewhere in the middle. But it will stay the same always.

So you can see why it is easy to lose track of time in a cave. But you brought a watch. And it's getting late. Better head for the cave's opening while your lights are still working! There'll be many more caves to explore. Maybe the next time you'll pick an ice cave!

The Summer House Secret

Hettie Jones

The rain had stopped. Now only the stream and the drip drip of the trees could be heard in the warm afternoon. Kate sat reading the letter from Alice Smith again.

"Go on outdoors, Kate. The sun's out," Aunt Isabel called from the kitchen.

Kate didn't move. *Strange things sure do happen in the city,* she read. *Last night our house was broken into and some papers were moved around in Daddy's office. The police came! Can you imagine coming home and finding your front door all broken?*

"Kate Gordon!" Aunt Isabel yelled. "Out!"

Kate jumped up and ran outside, pushing the letter into her pocket. "Nothing strange ever happens here in Shadow Lake," she sighed, walking slowly along the stream.

A mile down, the stream ran into Shadow
Lake, which gave its name to the town where
Kate lived. She liked Shadow Lake in summer,
when people came from the city. But in winter
it was dull. Her only fun was making up stories
to scare her mother and aunt, like the one
about the lion she saw. It turned out to be
Mrs. Rico's cat.

SMITH

Kate went on around the lake until she came
to a sign that said SMITH. Not far
away she could see some men getting Lake
Road ready for summer. The countryside was
nearly ready, too, Kate noticed. The color of
the leaves and flowers appeared different, even
more beautiful, after the rain.

Alice had written that her family would be at the lake in four weeks. Kate walked up the path to the Smith's house. "I wish Alice were here right now," she thought.

The big house stood quiet and closed, as if it were sleeping. "That noisy boy will wake you up soon," she said, thinking of Alice's little brother Tom.

Kate sat down to rest on a stone bench near the house. Taking out the letter, she read again: *Four more weeks and then — just you and me and the old s.p. — remember?*

How could Kate forget! The letters s.p. stood for "secret passageway." It was in the Smith house, and it went all the way from the cellar to the second floor. Every summer Kate and Alice would hide there when they wanted to get away from Tom. It was their special place, and they had written their names on the wall.

"I wish I could look at our names," Kate thought. Then she noticed that one of the cellar windows was open a crack. She ran over and opened it all the way. It would be easy to get to the passageway!

Kate looked around at the bench, the path, the field of flowers and waving grass. She felt as if she were the only one around for miles. Should she climb in?

Suddenly a loud sound came from over by Lake Road. Was that the men working — or thunder? "If it rains, I'll be better off inside," Kate thought. Another boom came from the lake. She turned back to the open window and quickly crawled through.

Kate counted stones along the cellar wall, and then pushed hard on the third one she touched. With a dull scraping sound a door swung open, and she tiptoed up the stairs of the secret passageway.

At the second floor the stairs opened onto a room with a tiny window. Just below the window were their names. Kate smiled. Then she hit the inside wall once. Another small secret door banged open, and she crawled through it into Alice's room.

White sheets covered the bed, table, and chairs. Kate went out to the hall and looked down at the first floor. Everything in the living room was covered, too. Next to the living room was Mr. Smith's workshop.

Through the open door she saw his drawing table, piled high with papers and tools. Mr. Smith was an architect. He sometimes worked there during the winter or sent his helpers to use the workshop. Kate often saw their cars in front of the house.

The workshop had a lot of tools that Kate wanted to touch. She was so busy looking that she didn't even hear the car coming up the drive. Quickly she ran back to Alice's room and looked out the window. "Oh no," she breathed. "Someone's here!" A blue car stopped at the house, and a man got out.

"Mr. Smith must have sent an architect," she thought. The man started up to the front door.

Her heart racing, Kate jumped away from the window. What if he had seen her? What would people think, finding her in the Smith house? They would never let her come here again! Alice wouldn't talk to her any more! She had to get away!

But how? She could hide in the secret passageway until he went, but what if he stayed for a long time? Mama would worry so if she didn't get home by dark. Kate's eyes filled with tears. No, it would be impossible to hide for long. She *must* get away.

A loud noise made her jump. What was he doing? Quietly Kate crawled out to the hall and lay on the floor staring down at the workshop. The light over the table had been turned on. Mr. Smith's tools were all over the floor. While she watched, the man picked up one paper after another. He looked at each one and then threw it down angrily.

Kate was so amazed that for a second she couldn't think. Why was he acting so strange? Then she remembered what Alice had written: *Last night our house was broken into and some papers were moved around in Daddy's office...* "He can't be an architect!" Kate thought suddenly. "He must be the man who Alice wrote about!"

Suddenly her heart was pounding and she felt really scared. She crawled back through Alice's room to the passageway and ran down the stairs.

In the cellar she could still hear things falling. Quickly she climbed out the window and fell onto the wet grass.

In the twilight the field of flowers looked gray. "Oh, goodness, it's late," Kate thought. Then she ran for her life, past the stone bench and out to the dark river road.

A Chase in the Dark

"Don't worry, Winifred, she'll be along,"
Aunt Isabel was saying to Kate's mother.

"But Isabel, Kate's always home long before
this. It's already dark!"

Outside, their dog began barking. The women
ran to the door. Kate came running up the
path, out of breath.

"Where have you been?" asked Kate's mother.

"Whatever happened?" Aunt Isabel asked.

Kate could hardly talk. "A man...in the
Smith house...a robber..."

"Kate, you know Mr. Smith often sends his
men to the workshop," Aunt Isabel said.

Kate jumped up. "No, he was throwing Mr.
Smith's papers around. It sounds crazy, but
I know he's not an architect—he's the man
who broke into their house in the city.
I just *know* it."

"What are you talking about?" her mother
laughed.

82

Kate told them about Alice's letter. Aunt Isabel still looked puzzled. "Kate, how could you see into the workshop? Those windows are way over your head."

It was a while before Kate answered. "I went inside the house through the secret passageway," she said at last.

Kate's mother stared. "Secret passageway?... But why?" she asked.

"I missed Alice and I just wanted to see our names," Kate answered, ready to cry. "But then the man came, and I got really scared watching him throw Mr. Smith's papers on the floor." Kate turned to her aunt. "It must be important! In the city the police came..."

Aunt Isabel looked at Kate. There could be some truth to the child's story for once.

"Winifred, where are the car keys?" she asked in an excited voice.

"Isabel, do you really think we should?" Kate's mother asked.

"We *must*," said Isabel, and that decided it. All three of them ran to the car and jumped in. Kate was excited. At last something was happening in Shadow Lake!

As they bounced along the dark road near the Smith house, Kate heard a car starting up. "He's leaving!" she shouted. Suddenly the blue car came out of the drive and turned into Lake Road.

"That's him! Let's chase him, Aunt Isabel!"

"Stop shouting!" Aunt Isabel yelled. She put on the bright headlights. When the man saw that they were tailing him, he began to speed.

Kate's mother saw the signs first. "Isabel, watch out!" she screamed. Ahead, a police car's red light swung around. A truck blocked the road where the men were still working. Unable to stop in time, the blue car hit the truck. Aunt Isabel brought their car to a stop a few feet away.

Officer Greenly came over to them. "Miss Belt! And Mrs. Gordon—and Kate, too! What on earth…"

Aunt Isabel was pleased to see that the man in the blue car had not been hurt. "Officer Greenly," she ordered, "make sure that man doesn't get away!"

Officer Greenly looked puzzled. "Will you please get out and explain this?" she asked.

"Indeed I will," Aunt Isabel said. "Come, Kate." They walked over to the blue car.

The man stared at them angrily. "Listen," he told Officer Greenly, "the whole thing happened because of these crazy women. I was just driving along when I noticed a car following me. I thought someone wanted to rob me so I tried to get away."

"Is this the man, Kate?" Aunt Isabel asked. "The one in the workshop?"

"Yes," answered Kate, hardly able to look at him.

Kate's mother joined them and she explained, "Kate is sure that she saw this man in Ross Smith's workshop throwing papers around. And someone broke into Ross's city office last week."

"How could Kate see into the workshop?" asked Officer Greenly. "Those windows are high." She was puzzled.

"That's another story," Kate's mother said. "We'll explain later. But I do think Kate is telling the truth. He may have been after something."

"Well, in that case," Officer Greenly said to the man, "may we have a look in your car?"

"I won't say another word until I see my lawyer!" yelled the man.

"That's your right," said Kate.

"Where did you learn that?" her mother asked.

"In school," Kate answered proudly. Suddenly she noticed some papers on the back seat of the man's car. "Look," she pointed. Aunt Isabel pressed her nose against the window.

"These are blueprints," she said excitedly. "And they say 'State Building' at the top. Ross is going to be very surprised."

"I'll say," said Officer Greenly. "Why don't you go home now. I'll take this man in and give Ross a call. We'll be at your house later."

Kate's mother smiled at her. "I'll make tea, Officer Greenly. You'll need it by then."

Kate could hardly keep her eyes open by the time everyone came later that night.

"Got here as soon as I could," Mr. Smith said. "Can't imagine how unhappy I am. That Ben Potter worked for me for two years. Suddenly quit three weeks ago. Awful."

"But why did he take the blueprints?" Aunt Isabel asked.

"To copy them and try to get the State House job himself," Mr. Smith sighed. "Might have done it too, if you hadn't stopped him!" He smiled at Kate.

"Kate," said Officer Greenly, "you never told me how you saw Potter. Those windows are..."

"My first thought too, Officer Greenly," laughed Aunt Isabel. "But she'll tell you."

Everyone looked at Kate. "Do you want a lawyer?" Kate's mother asked, smiling.

"No, Mama," Kate smiled back. Then she explained. "I went into the house through the secret passageway. When the man came and I saw him throwing things, I got scared and ran."

"Well, you'd better not snoop around summer houses anymore," Officer Greenly said, "or one day you *will* need a lawyer."

Kate's mother laughed. "Right now I think what she needs is some sleep."

In bed, Kate thought of how she would tell the story. "Imagine, Alice," she would say, "this is the truth—there we were, chasing him in the dark, while Potter fired shot after shot down the middle of Lake Road..."

And that's when Kate fell asleep.

A Space in a

If you could build a house,
any kind of house, anywhere
you wished, what kind would
it be? Where would it be?

Would it be underwater in the ocean
in a pretty coral cave?

Would it be high up on a mountain with
the nimble-footed goats?

Would it be in a valley near a river
or a stream?

Would it be underground with the
rabbits and the moles?

Would it be in a tree with the
leaves and the birds and wind?

Would it be on a beach near the
crying of the gulls?

Place for You

Would it be in the desert with the cactus and the sand?

Would it be on the ranchlands where you'd hear coyotes call?

Would it be in outer space with the comets and the stars?

Or would you make a houseboat to go down the river far away?

Write a story about your house. Try to make it a "word picture."

Empty Buildings, Empty Streets

Judith Adams

If you had a day to explore any place you liked, what kind of place would you pick? A secret passageway? A cave? A strange country? Outer space? A ghost town? Have you ever heard of ghost towns?

Some ghost towns are places where a few people live with the ghosts of thousands of people who once made the town a busy, noisy place.

And some towns have just disappeared without a trace. But most ghost towns are places where old, empty buildings still stand. No one lives in these ghost towns. Think of all the fun you could have exploring those old buildings and walking down those empty streets!

Cripple Creek, Colorado

What brought thousands of people to a town in the first place? And what made so many of them leave after a while? GOLD. More than one hundred years ago, a lot of gold was found in the West. People from all over the country went to get some. Wherever they stopped, people pitched tents and began to mine for gold. Everyone had high hopes and strong backs. But most of the people who looked for gold found little or none. So they packed up their things and moved on, looking for gold somewhere else.

If a place turned out to have a lot of gold, before long the tents would come down. Houses and other buildings would go up. Then more people would come, not to mine for gold, but to build stores and banks and other things that a town needs. In this way, some towns grew. Some people made a lot of money.

Every ghost town has its own special story. Take Cripple Creek, Colorado. Cripple Creek stands on the edge of a volcano that is millions of years old. Millions of years ago, the volcano burst. When it burst, lava from the volcano covered pockets of gold. For millions of years after that, the gold stayed out of sight, deep under the lava.

When people came west to Colorado looking for gold, they didn't look for it where the old volcano had been. All they could see there was grassy ranchland. No one looked there. But then, in 1890, a young cowboy did look. And he found gold in the dead volcano. At first, people didn't believe his story of gold. But after a while they did, and they came running. That was the beginning of Cripple Creek.

Cripple Creek became the second largest gold mining spot in the whole world! At one time about 50,000 people lived there. But in time it cost too much to run the mines. Many mines had to close down. And slowly, the noisy, busy mining town became a ghost town.

Cripple Creek didn't disappear. But today only a few hundred people live there. Some of the mines are still running, and some people believe there is still a lot of gold to be found. If you walked down the main street, you might meet a miner who remembers the "old days." Who knows? He may believe that there is new gold to be found. He may share his dream of once again making Cripple Creek the second greatest gold mining town in the world.

THE HAMMER OF THUNDER

Ann Pyk

Long ago, in the far, far North, there were two kingdoms in the sky. One was the home of the gods, the other the home of the giants. The gods and the giants were not friends. The greedy giants made the gods afraid. And the giants were afraid of the magic of the gods.

In the land of gods, there were all kinds of gods. There were gods of fun and tricks. There were beautiful gods, kind gods, wise ones, and strong ones. But in the land of giants, there were only big, greedy giants.

The strongest of all the gods was Thor, the god of thunder. And the biggest and greediest of all giants was Thrym. Thor had a magic hammer. He carried it wherever he went, making thunder with it throughout the sky. His hammer made him stronger than Thrym. With it he kept the kingdom of the gods safe from the giants.

The gods and the giants were almost always angry with each other. Their fights were terrible and many. But all had been quiet for a while, until one morning...

Thor got up and found his hammer was gone. He gave an angry roar as he ran to find the god of fun and tricks.

"Loki, did you take my hammer?" he cried.

"I did not," answered Loki. "My tricks are made for playing on giants, not gods."

"Who then could have taken my hammer?" cried Thor. "Our kingdom is not safe. The giants will come and take our houses, our goats, and our gold. Oh, where's my magic hammer?"

"Let's ask Freya," said Loki. "Maybe she knows where it is."

And so they ran to Freya.

"Freya, did you see my magic hammer?" asked Thor.

She shook her head. The beautiful Freya did not know where it was.

"What shall we do?" cried Thor. "Without the hammer the giants will come and take our home."

"Loki, take my coat of feathers," said Freya, "and fly down to the land of the giants. They must have taken the hammer."

"Good idea!" said Loki. "I will find those giants and get the hammer. Don't worry."

With the feather coat, Loki flew down to the cave of the great giant Thrym.

Loki landed at the mouth of the cave. He found Thrym combing a horse.

"That horse once belonged to the kingdom of the gods," said Loki. Thrym looked up from his work.

"Ah! It is Loki, I see," said Thrym. "And what brings you to the land of the giants?"

"The gods are angry," answered Loki. "Someone has taken Thor's magic hammer."

"Ho! Ho! I have it!" cried Thrym, laughing. "And I have put it eight miles deep in the earth."

"Return it at once!" shouted Loki.

"Am I a fool?" asked Thrym. "Oh, no. Not until you bring me the beautiful Freya to be my wife. Only then will Thor have his hammer."

"You are mad!" cried Loki. "Freya will never marry you."

"Then you will not see the hammer again," roared the giant.

At first Loki stared at the huge, laughing giant. Then he turned to leave.

The sound of Thrym's awful laugh followed Loki as he flew back to Freya and Thor.

When Freya heard that she must marry the terrible giant, she screamed. "Never! Never! I will never marry Thrym!" And her beads fell into a hundred pieces of anger as she ran away.

"I would never want our beautiful Freya to marry that terrible giant!" said Thor sadly.

"But we are lost without the hammer," said Loki.

"Yes, we are lost," said Thor. For a while no one said a word.

"Maybe Heimdall can help us," said Loki suddenly.

They called on the wise Heimdall for help.
And Heimdall gathered all the gods to think.
For nine days and nights they thought.
At last the wise Heimdall had an idea.

"Why not send Thor dressed as the beautiful
Freya?" he said.

"I, the god of thunder, dressed as a bride?"
cried Thor.

"Of course!" said Loki joyfully. "We will play
a trick on the giant. You will be the bride.
And I will dress as your bridesmaid!"

"Never!" shouted Thor. "Silly idea! Foolish!"

"But it will work. I know it will," said Loki.

"Well—we must try something," said Thor.
"I must have my magic hammer. I will do it."

And so the plans were made.

Thor was dressed as a bride, with a veil to
hide his angry eyes.

"The giant Thrym will never know who we are," laughed Loki. "You will see."

In no time, the "bride" and her "bridesmaid" flew down through the sky to the land of the greedy giants.

When Thrym saw the gods' royal horses, he shouted, "Freya, my love, you have come at last! I have had all things to please me but a beautiful bride. Now I shall have that, too."

Thor stood quietly beside the smiling giant. He didn't say a word.

Thrym ordered a huge wedding dinner. The food was made for giants, but his little bride ate like a giant as well. She ate a huge cow, then eight huge fish. She also drank three tubs of mead.

"How can my little bride eat and drink so much?" asked Thrym.

"She fasted for nine days and nights while longing to marry you!" said the bridesmaid quickly. "That is why she eats so much."

"Ah-haaaaa!" laughed Thrym as he kissed his bride. But then he saw those angry eyes.

"How can my little bride have such angry, red eyes?" asked the giant.

Again the bridesmaid quickly said, "She could not sleep for nine days and nights. That is why her eyes are red."

The giant smiled.

Suddenly, the giant stood up. Pounding the table, he looked down at his little bride.

"BRING THE MAGIC HAMMER!" he ordered. "We will hold it in our hands as we marry. It will bring us joy forever and an end to the kingdom of the gods!"

Thor waited.

The hammer was brought to the table. Thrym stretched out his arm to take it. At the same time, Thor stretched out his arm.

The second he touched the hammer, Thor pulled off his veil. He laughed a laugh like thunder. Lightning flew from his eyes. He was strong again. He killed the giant Thrym and all the other greedy giants.

Thor had the magic hammer. Once more the kingdom of the gods was safe.

The trick had worked. And Thor and Loki flew laughing through the sky. They made thunder and lightning all the way home.

What On Earth Did Children Play With?

Hilary Beckett

Pretend you were a child many years ago, long before television was invented; long before the toys you have now were invented. What would you have played with?

Well, children knew how to play, even thousands of years ago. They used whatever they found around them — the same things you can find around you — sand, water, air, trees, and rocks. They knew how to use small stones and seeds for games. They knew how to draw on the soft ground with sticks, branches, and fingers. They knew how to make whistles out of grass by holding the grass a special way in their fingers. And children thousands of years ago had each other — just as you do today.

LARRY ROSS

Pretend you are a child thousands of years ago in a warm country not far from an ocean.

You wake up in the morning and go to find a friend.

"What shall we play today?" your friend asks.

"Oh, I don't know," you say. Remember, you have no bike, no balloons, no baseball and bat, no small racing cars, and no television. These things haven't been invented yet. "Let's dig a hole in the ground and pitch cherry stones in it."

"But I don't like cherries," your friend says. "I hate to eat cherries. They make me sick. Couldn't we have a race over to that tree? Then I won't have to eat cherries."

"Well, racing makes *me* sick," you say. "It's too hot. I'll tell you what. Let's draw straws. If you get the long straw, we'll race. If you get the short straw, I get to choose a game I want."

You hold the straws behind your back. You're out of luck! Your friend wins. So you race to the tree, but she is faster.

"Let's go to the beach where the wind is cool," you say. "I'm out of breath."

You cross the hot sand to the water. Your feet feel good when the waves run up over them. You decide to make a sand castle with a wall around it. But then the sea carries away your castle, so you decide to look for stones and skip them in the water. Your friend is busy collecting stones for another game — white stones and black ones.

After she's found them, you make two big lines in the sand with your feet. Then you make two more lines, so the sand looks like this:

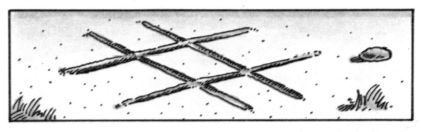

You choose the black stones, your friend chooses the white. It's your turn first. You put your stone in the corner. At the end of the game the sand looks like this:

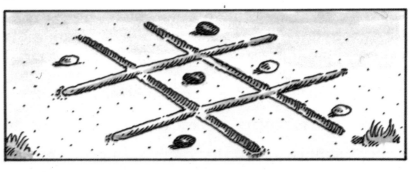

Can you guess who wins?

Then you yell, "I'm the King of the Castle!" as you run up the hill from the beach. At the top you and your friend pretend to push each other off. Then you sit and play "Odds and Evens."

When you play "Odds and Evens," you hold your hands behind your back and guess "Odds!" or "Evens!" as you put out one or two or more fingers on each hand and quickly bring them in front. Everyone's fingers are counted. It's a game any number can play. You win if your guess ("Odds!" or "Evens!") is right.

More friends come along. You whistle to them and they come over. You all decide to play "Follow the Leader."

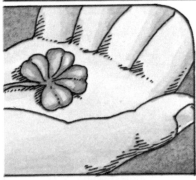

You slide down the hill behind the leader and cross the river on a log. You climb trees. You run through fields. "Look! I've found a four-leaf clover!" You kneel in the grass, and the others stop to look.

"That clover is really lucky," everyone says. "There aren't too many around."

Then you all play tag and hiding games. And you sit and make grass whistles....

...You spent a whole day without television, bikes, or other ready-made toys. What on earth did you find to play with?

Naming Things

How and why things got their names is very interesting. Why are stalactites called stalactites? Stalagmites, stalagmites?

If you had to name things in order to talk about them, how would you do it? Would you name them for what they look like? What they sound like? Or what they do?

Try to think of names for these things.

The Big Pile of Dirt

Eleanor Clymer

On our street there was an empty lot. It was small, but it was full of junk. There was an armchair with the stuffing coming out. There were boxes and tires and other things that people didn't want. And in the middle was a big pile of dirt. But I better not start telling you about that yet. First I will tell how we got started with the lot. It was like this.

See, we live in this old apartment building. There's me. My name is Mike. I'm the oldest in my family. I have a sister, Arleen, and two brothers, twins, five years old. Their names are Billy and Sam. After school Arleen watches them, when my mother is working. I have to help her sometimes, when they act up.

I have some friends who live in the building. My two best friends are Joe and Russ. We go to school together, and we're on the basketball team. After school we go somewhere and play.

That's where the trouble started. There wasn't any place to play. We couldn't all play in some-one's apartment. There's no room. The apart-ments have too much stuff in them——beds and things.

If we played ball in the street, the little kids would run out after the ball. They could get hurt that way. When Arleen tells them not to, they don't listen to her. They listen to me all right, but I can't mind them all the time.

Sometimes we went up on the roof. It was nice there. You felt high up, close to the sky. You could see the tall buildings way downtown and the boats on the river. You could see white birds flying around. I liked to watch them.

But there's this lady, Mrs. Crane. Her wash got stolen once. So after that they made us get off the roof.

And besides, it was no place for Billy and Sam. They might fall off. Let's face it. I couldn't get rid of them. Arleen couldn't handle them alone.

Then we tried to play in the side court. But Mrs. Giotto, who lived in 2A on that side, was mad at us because we laughed at her because she was fishing. I mean it. She really was.

See, it was a windy day, and she had her wash on a line outside her window. Some clothes blew down into the court. She leaned out of the window with a ball of string and a hook and let down the hook and fished up a dress. When she let down the hook again, we put an old sock on it. Mrs. Giotto looked pretty funny fishing out the window. We couldn't help laughing. So then she was mad at us and always told us to get out of the court.

Once we went down to the furnace room. It was warm there, and the furnace was like a giant with one big eye and a mouth full of fire. It was scary, but nice. But it was no use. The Super came and said, "The furnace room is no place for you. All you kids——out!"

We had to find a place. And it had to be a place where all of us could go. Well, right next to our house there was an empty house. No one lived in it because it wasn't safe. The house was all ready to fall down, and the doors and windows were covered with boards. One day some men came with trucks and tore it down. We all stood around and watched.

They put up boards to stand on, and the men climbed up and pulled pieces out of the walls. You could see inside where the bedrooms were. You could see the stairs and the kitchens.

Well, when they got through, there was nothing there but an empty lot with some bricks and old boards in it. But it didn't stay empty long. People would throw things in it——broken dishes and cans, and all the things people don't want. Or else they would come out at night and throw things there when they thought no one was looking. They put this old armchair out there, and tires and lots of other stuff.

Every day my friends and I would go and see what was there. We found some good things. I found a hammer that the men had left. And Johnny was lucky. He found a baseball bat that looked as good as new.

This was in summer, so we played there all day every day. Joe and Russ and I made a fort out of bricks. We had to watch that the twins didn't get hurt with the broken glass and nails that were all around the lot. Arleen's friend Margie came with her little sister, and she would put things in her mouth if you didn't look out.

But still it was a pretty good place. We made a swing for the little kids out of an old tire. We hung it from some poles we drove in the ground.

And all the time we were waiting for someone to tell us to get out, but no one did.

How the Dirt Came to the Lot

One day when we were playing, some ladies came. They came in a car with a man. They all got out and stood looking at our lot. We watched them and heard what they said.

One lady said, "This is a mess. Look at all that broken glass and junk."

Another lady said, "That is no place for these children."

A third lady said, "How can we have a beautiful city with places like this? Mr. Mayor, you must do something."

I thought to myself, "Could that be the Mayor?" I got ready for him to run us out.

But he didn't. He just said to the ladies, "All right, I'll give orders for something to be done." Then they went away.

Joe said, "Now what? Will they make us get out?"

"No," I said, "they just want to clean it."

Arleen said, "That means we get out. I knew it."

"Well, wait and see," I said. But I was afraid she was right.

That is not what happened, though. Something different happened. One day a big truck came. It was full of dirt. Two men got out and looked at our empty lot.

One said, "Is this the place, Mac?"

The other said, "Looks like it."

The first one said, "Are we supposed to dump the dirt here?"

The other said, "Those are the orders."
The first one said, "Then let her go."

They backed up the truck onto our lot.
Then they let her go. They dumped all that
dirt right in the middle of our lot. It made
a noise like thunder. When they were finished,
the men went away.

Joe asked, "What's it all about?"

I said, "I don't know."

We waited for something else to happen.
But nothing happened. I went and stuck my
hand in the dirt. It was nice and soft. It
was clean dirt. It seemed like someone wanted
to give us a present. I thought we might
as well have some fun with it.

So I said, "Come on, kids."

Then we started playing. We climbed up
the pile of dirt. I stood on top and said, "I am
the President." Joe came behind me and gave
me a push. I went down the dirt pile.

Then I had a great idea. I found a garbage can cover. I climbed to the top of the pile of dirt and slid down. Pretty soon all the kids were doing it.

Then we started digging. We got some pieces of board and some cans to dig with. The little kids were busy filling up old pots and dishes with dirt and making cakes. Joe, Russ, and I hadn't played in dirt for a long time, but we did it, too, just like the little kids. It was fun.

Some girls found flowers in a garbage can. They planted them in the dirt, and Margie said, "This is going to be like a park. Don't pick the flowers."

Arleen said, "If it's a park, there should be benches for people to sit on." So we made benches out of old boards. Then we pulled the old armchair up to the top of the pile. We took turns sitting in it.

I said, "Whoever is the President can sit in it." So every day another kid was President. He could sit in the chair and give orders to the other kids.

One day it rained. I thought, "Now it will be all mud and wash away." But it wasn't. It was like sand. The water ran through it and left it a little wet. It was better than ever. You could mold things out of it. I made a man's head and stuck an old hat on it.

Well, we kept waiting for something to happen to our pile of dirt, but nothing did, so we forgot. We just thought about it as if it was ours.

It got to be winter, and we made a snow-man on top.

Then spring came and it got warm. One day Margie started to yell, "Look! Something is growing!"

We looked, and there was green grass on one side of the dirt.

Margie said, "Don't touch it, you kids. Keep off the grass." The kids took care not to step on Margie's grass.

Then Arleen said, "We should have trees." But where could we get trees?

One day Johnny found a can of paint. He painted trees on the wall of the building next to the lot. It looked good. It was almost too good to be true, which is what my mother says sometimes.

Mike Meets the Mayor

One day when we were playing, a car stopped
and the same ladies got out. A man was with
them——the same Mayor.

I said to the kids, "Hide, fast." So we
hid and watched. The ladies looked at our
pile of dirt. One of them got mad.

She said, "Mr. Mayor, you said you would
have this place cleaned up, but nothing has
been done."

The Mayor said, "Yes, I remember. I gave
orders to clean it up, but someone dumped
a pile of dirt in the lot. I bet someone else
is still waiting for that pile of dirt."

Another lady said, "Those children are still
playing in the lot. It's a dangerous place
to play in."

The Mayor said, "Yes, you're right. It is
dangerous. We'll have it cleaned up and a
fence put around it."

Joe said, "Are they going to take away our pile of dirt?"

Arleen said, "They can't."

Two little kids started to cry.

I said, "Keep still, you kids. Let me think." The ladies were pointing at our things and talking. The Mayor kept shaking his head. I thought, "I have to do something."

Then, before I could think anymore, I marched out. I felt as if someone was pushing me, only no one was. I walked right in front of them and said, "Please leave our stuff alone."

They all looked surprised. The Mayor said, "What's this? Who are you?"

I said, "I'm just one of the kids. This is our pile of dirt. We play here. Please don't take it away."

The Mayor said, "Is it all right if we look at it?"

I said, "Sure." So they went in the lot and looked at all the junk we had there.

The Mayor said, "You see, children, we want to clean this place up."

I said, "We like it this way." I was awfully scared. I thought maybe he could send me to jail for talking like that. But I had to say it. I thought, "They're going to take it away from us, and there's nothing we can do. There's no one to help us."

But all of a sudden we heard a voice. "What's wrong? Did the kids do something?"

We all looked up and there was Mrs. Giotto, leaning out of her window. She said, "Wait, I'll be right down." It didn't take her long to get down.

She said, "Those kids are not hurting anyone. You leave them alone."

I sure was surprised. She wasn't mad at us after all! The Mayor and the ladies were surprised, too.

One lady said, "But don't you see, this lot is dangerous."

Mrs. Giotto said, "No one got hurt here yet. Those kids have no place to play. You should leave them alone."

Then the Super came out. He said, "They don't get into trouble any more. It's a good thing for them."

Then I saw my mother coming home from work. When she saw all the people, she got scared. "What happened?" she asked.

Arleen said, "We're all right, Mama. But they want to clean up our pile of dirt."

Mama said, "Clean it up? What for? It's all right the way it is."

And suddenly I thought, "What do you know! They're all on our side! They're all fighting for us!"

The Mayor looked at us standing there. Then he looked at the ladies. And then he smiled all over his face.

He said, "You know what? I have a great idea. We'll make a park here for the kids."

Then everyone began to smile, too, and nod their heads. And Mrs. Giotto said, "Now you're talking."

The Mayor said, "We'll clean it up and put in benches and swings and pipes to crawl through and things to climb on. How would you like that, children?"

We stood there and couldn't say a word. It was too sudden. But then Billy said, "What about our pile of dirt?"

The Mayor said, "Well, I don't know. It's hard to keep a pile of dirt clean. It gets all over everything."

Then I got brave and said, "We don't care. We like it." And all the other kids nodded their heads.

So the Mayor thought a while, and then he said, "I tell you what. We'll move the pile of dirt over to one side and put some new dirt on it. We'll build a little fence around it, and you can still have it. And we'll make a little pool for you. How's that?"

It was our turn to think a while. Then Margie said, "What about the grass on the pile?" and Johnny said, "What about the painting on the wall?"

The mayor said, "We could move the grass over, or we could give you some seeds to plant new grass. And we'll keep the painting. We could even give you more paint and you could paint the rest of the wall."

So we said all right.

Well, the next week the men got to work. They cleaned it all up. They moved the dirt into the back of the lot. They put in benches and swings, just like they said. And they put in pipes to crawl through and big stone animals you could climb on or just sit under and think, if you wanted to. They planted trees and flowers. And Margie put a little fence around her grass and even planted her own flowers.

And we painted the walls. We made trees and lions and all kinds of things.

It is a very good park, and everyone is proud of it. All the people on our street came to a party there. They take care of it and don't throw junk in it either. We sure needed that park.

But sometimes I go there by myself, early in the morning, or when it has just rained, and there aren't so many other people around. And I pretend. I pretend it's the way it used to be, just a big pile of dirt in the middle of an empty lot.

Spaces and Places

Spaces where I do what I like to do
Are fun to change around.
I like to play football in the house once in a while.
Sometimes I like to sleep outdoors on the ground.

I like to hang my coat on the floor
And keep my gerbil in the coat closet instead.
I like to read at the top of a tall tree.
I like to drink chocolate shakes in my bed.

I've heard my parents say
That everything has its own place.
But as for me, I always like to think of how to
        change around
            the places where I do
                what I like to do and
                    find a *new*
                        use for an *old* space.

—Hilary Beckett

GLOSSARY

This glossary will help you in pronouncing and understanding the meanings of unusual or difficult words in this book. If you need help in pronouncing the words, use the key at the bottom of each right-hand page.

PRONUNCIATION KEY

Symbol	Key Words
a	at, bad
ā	ape, care, pain, day
ä	father, car
e	end, pet
ē	me, feet, meat, piece, finally
i	it, pig
ī	ice, lie, my
o	odd, on, hot
ō	old, oat, low, toe
ô	coffee, fork, author, law, all
oo	wood, put
o͞o	fool, true
oi	oil, boy
ou	out, cow
u	up, mud, oven
yo͞o	use, cue, few, feud
ur	turn, term, bird, word
ə	a *in* ago
	e *in* taken
	i *in* pencil
	o *in* lemon
	u *in* helpful
b	bat, above, job

Symbol	Key Words
ch	chin, such, hatch
d	dear, soda, bad
f	five, defend, leaf, off
g	game, ago, fog
h	hit, ahead
j	joke, enjoy, gem, edge
k	kit, baking, seek, tack, cat
l	lid, sailor, feel, ball
m	man, family, dream
n	not, final, on
ng	singer, long, sink
p	pail, repair, soap
r	ride, parent, four
s	sat, aside, cats, cent, pass
sh	shoe, wishing, fish
t	tag, pretend, hat
th	thin, both
th	this, mother, smooth
v	very, favor
w	wet, reward
y	yes
z	zoo, gazing, rose, dogs
zh	treasure, seizure, garage

A

a·maze (ə māz′) to cause to feel great surprise.

an·ten·nas (an ten′əz) metal wires used to send or pick up radio and television sounds and pictures.

aq·ua·naut (ak′wə nôt) one who has been trained to study underwater life.

arch·i·tect (är′ kə tekt) a person who plans buildings and sees that the plans are carried out by the builders.

B

Bach (bäk)

beau·ti·ful (byo̅o̅′ ti fəl) very pleasant to look at or hear.

be·lov·ed (bi luv′ id) much loved.

blueprints (blo̅o̅′prints) blue and white drawings used mostly for architects' plans.

bow (bō) a long, thin stick with horse hairs stretched end to end, used for playing instruments of the violin family.

bow (bou) to bend the upper part of the body forward.

burst (burst) to break open or fly apart suddenly.

C

cel·lar (sel′ ər) a room or rooms underground, most often under a building.

cel·lo (chel′ ō) a large musical instrument of the violin family.

cor·al (kôr′ əl) a stony underwater growth that looks like a plant.

Co·rel·li (kō′ rel ē)

court (kôrt) an open space with buildings or walls around it.

crea·ture (krē′ chər) a living being; any person or animal.

D

dan·ger·ous (dān′ jər əs) likely to cause harm.

dis·ap·pear (dis′ ə pēr) to stop being seen.

drugs (drugz) pills and other things used to fight sickness.

E

ex·cit·ed (ik sī′ tid) stirred up.

ex·pect (ik spekt′) to think that something will happen or come; to look forward to.

ex·plain (iks plān′) to make clear or plain.

at, āpe, fäther; end, mē; īce; odd, ōld, côffee; wood, fo̅o̅l; oil, out; up, turn; ə for a in ago, e in taken, i in pencil, o in lemon, u in helpful; chin; singer; thin, this; zh = s in treasure.

ex·plore (iks plôr′) to travel to an unknown place in order to find out about it.

F

fare·well (fer wel′) good-by and good luck.

fast·ed (fast′ id) ate little or no food.

fi·nal·ly (fīn′ əl ē) at the end; at last.

flip·pers (flip′ ərz) wide, flat rubber shoes that swimmers wear to help them swim faster and easier.

Frey·a (frā′ ə)

fur·nace (fur′ nis) something in which heat to warm a building is made by burning coal or gas.

G

gods (godz) in olden times, beings who were supposed to have special power over people and the world.

grain (grān) small hard seeds used for food.

H

Hand·el (hand′ əl)

harp·si·chord (harp′ sə kôrd) a musical instrument that looks like a small piano, but sounds somewhat like a guitar.

Heim·dall (hām′ däl)

I

in·stru·ment (in′ strə mənt) something used for making music.

in·vent·ed (in vent′ əd) thought up or made something for the first time.

K

key·board (kē′ bôrd) a row, or rows, of keys on a piano or typewriter.

L

lac·quer (lak′ ər) a paint that dries fast and is very shiny.

laun·dry (lôn′ drē) a place where clothes are washed.

la·va (la′ və) hot, melted rock that bursts out of a volcano.

law·yer (lô′ yər) a person who makes his living advising people about the law, and acting for them in court.

le·gend (lej′ ənd) a story that has been handed down through the years.

140

Lo·ki (lō′ kē)

M

ma·chine (mə shēn′) a thing made up of fixed and moving parts for doing some kind of work. (a sewing machine).

man·aged (man′ ijd) was able to.

mead (mēd) a strong drink made of honey, water, and dried leaves.

mold (mōld) to give shape to. (He liked to mold animals in clay with his hands.)

mouth·piece (mouth′ pēs) a part or a piece of a musical instrument placed in or near the mouth.

N

nat·u·ral (nach′ ər əl) not made by people.

na·ture (nā′ chər) all things not made by people.

O

o·cean (ō′ shən) a large body of salt water.

oc·to·pus (ok′ tə pəs) a sea animal that has eight legs.

P

pan·el (pan′ əl) a board on which the dials and controls of an instrument are placed.

pass·age·way (pas′ ij wā) a way through which people or things can pass or move.

pit·y (pit′ ē) a feeling of sadness for another person's bad luck.

plan·et (plan′ it) huge solid ball in space that spins around the sun.

pres·sure (presh′ ər) the force with which one thing presses against another.

R

re·cord·er (ri kôr′ dər) *see* page 50.

S

Scar·lat·ti (skär lä′ tē)

space (spās) The planet Earth and everything and everyone on it are in *space*.

sta·lac·tites (stə lak′ tīts) *see* page 71.

sta·lag·mites (stə lag′ mīts) *see* page 72.

straw (strô) the dry stem of a plant.

sup·er (sōo′ pər) a short name for superintendent—the person who takes care of a large building.

---

at, āpe, fäther; end, mē; it, īce; odd, ōld, côffee; wood, fōol; oil, out; up, turn; ə for *a* in *ago*, e in *taken*, i in *pencil*, o in *lemon*, u in *helpful*; **ch**in; sin**g**er; **th**in; **th**is; **zh** = s in treasure.

T

tank (tangk) a large container for holding liquid or gas.

tem·per·a·ture (tem′ pər ə chər) the degree of hotness or coldness of something, such as the air or a person's body.

Thor (thôr)

throne (thrōn) the chair on which a king or queen sits.

Thrym (thrim)

trace (trās) something left behind that showed a person or thing had been there.

twi·light (twī′ līt) the dim light that comes just after the sun goes down.

V

valve (valv) a moving part that controls the flow of a gas or liquid.

Venice (ven′ is)

vi·o·la da gam·ba (vē ō′ lə də gam′- bə) a large stringed instrument.

vol·ca·no (vol kā′ nō) an opening in the earth from which lava is poured.

W

wa·ter·proof (wô′ tər pro͞of) able to hold out water.